SPECIALS!

Poetry

David Orme

Folens
Publishers

Acknowledgements

The author and publishers would like to thank the following for permission to reproduce poetry:

Su Andi for *Everybody Rap* from *Doin Mi Ed In* (Pan Macmillan)
Ian Blackman for *Losing Marker*
Adelaide Crapsey for *November Night*
Peter Dixon for *Dying Dog*
Toby Jugg for *Street Monsters*
Brian Moses for *Croc City Rap*
David Orme for *Liverpool Jam* and *Hi Mr Fly*
Phil Powley for *Having Kittens*
Levi Tafari for *Litter*
Ray Barker for haiku first published in *Schools Poetry Review Four*

First published 1994 by Folens Limited, Albert House, Apex Business Centre, Boscombe Road, Dunstable, LU5 4RL, England.

ISBN 1 85276677-8

Editor: Susan Ross   Illustrations: Philip Hodgson   Cover: The Image Bank

Printed in Singapore by Craft Print.

Contents

Teachers' Notes

Given the right approach, poetry is a valuable and enjoyable part of language work for pupils with special educational needs. Poetry is short, memorable, rhythmic and, at times, funny and subversive. The 'daffodils' image is long gone!

The materials in this book are designed to emphasise the following:

- **Collaborative learning, in groups or pairs.**
  Although the sheets can be used by pupils on their own, the involvement of a special needs assistant will enhance their value.
- **Speaking and listening.**
  This should develop through group discussion, on which guidance is given, and through performance. The poems have been specially selected for their suitability to be performed.
- **The techniques of poetry.**
  Rhythm, sound, form, syllable counting and imagery are explored through simple, practical tasks.
- **Drafting.**
  Many of the tasks encourage a more thoughtful choice of words and ideas through brainstorming and drafting.

Activity instructions and suggestions for follow-up work

Page 7 Get Into Shape
Develop by talking about other natural phenomena and objects, such as trees and rivers, that could be written as shape poems.

Page 8 Action Shapes
For the non-football minded, a word of explanation might be required here!

Page 9 Noisy Traffic
Eight is exceptional as the speeding objects will begin with the 'Ay' sound rather than the letter E. Use the alliterative pattern for other subjects, for example, animals. The numbers can be reversed, concluding with one, or none.

Page 10 Squelch!
Read *Jabberwocky* by Lewis Carroll as an introduction to neologisms.

Page 11 Sound Poems
Ensure pupils are able to differentiate the 'Shh...' words in the first sack from the hard C and K sounds in the second. Point out that some words can fit in either sack as they have both sounds. Talk about settings and situations that might be suitable for the words in the sacks. To follow up, provide an 'empty sack' for another sound group.

Page 12 Liverpool Jam
Rhyme can be a problem as pupils often assume that all poems must rhyme. This is dealt with by offering a range of both rhyming and non-rhyming poems. It is a pity to avoid rhyme altogether as it is part of the music of poetry and pupils like rhymes. Work on rhyme is valuable in developing auditory discrimination.

Page 13 Time For a Rhyme
These patterns demonstrate that rhyme does not have to be in couplet form, as in *Liverpool Jam*. Encourage pupils to continue their poems, using the same rhyme pattern.

Page 14 Line Up
Rhymes clearly indicate the lineation of a poem, and so the epitaph is easy to 'line up' (remember that *Fred Smith RIP* is the title, not part of the verse). Non-rhyming poems are more difficult. *Dustcart* is a haiku (5/7/5 syllables). The object is not necessarily to produce the right answer, but to discuss possibilities. *Deputy Head* has no fixed pattern.

Page 15 Tall Story
Once pupils have worked out the appropriate line they can design their own poem using the same starters, or by writing new ones.

Page 16 I've Got Rhythm
This is an extract from a classic nineteenth-century poem. If it is well received, find the full version and read it. The major purpose of looking at this is in developing an ear for the rhythm of the piece through performance. Some lines are quite tricky and will require practice. There is no correct answer to the question about the good news. The poem is not about a real historical event - Browning made the whole thing up!

Page 17 Get Rapping!
Much use is made of rap in this resource as it is popular with pupils and is a good medium for building confidence in speaking and listening.

Page 18 Sizzling Syllables
A syllable is difficult to define, but easy enough to understand. This exercise will help in that understanding. Regional dialect can add or lose syllables, as in the intrusive Y in whale (wayall).

Page 19 How Haiku Can You Go?
Insist that pupils try as hard as possible to achieve the correct pattern. The drafting and search for alternative words is a valuable exercise.

Pages 20-1 Limericks/Match Them Up
These activities explore a familiar pattern known by all pupils. Many will be able to quote limericks, but you may need to be broad minded!

Page 22 Poems Alive!
Exploring imagery can develop imaginative possibilities in the way pupils look at their own lives. The images here are similes, apart from 'wind' which is metaphorical.

Page 23 Riddles
Answers: hose, fish, fruit machine.

Page 24 Dirty Dustbins
Make sure pupils are familiar with the information on working in groups (see page 41) before tackling this activity. Emphasise that the questions on this sheet and on page 42 are discussion points, not questions requiring a definitive answer.

Page 25 First Lines
Encourage pupils to write non-rhyming poems for this exercise. Use *Dirty Dustbins* (page 24) as as example.

Page 26 Storytelling
If pupils cannot cope with writing down a dictated story, a cassette recorder can be used. This is an ideal exercise for a pupil working with a special needs assistant, who can act as scribe.

Page 27 Comic Strip Poem
The poems produced in *Time for a Rhyme* (see page 13) can be used for making comic strips.

Page 28 Telling a story
This is a traditional ballad, slightly cut and modernised and provides a possible starter for role play or story writing.

Page 29 Time For a Verb
Preparatory work on verbs may be required. In particular, pupils need to understand the concept of tense. The words given can be varied, for example, substitute shot for shoot/shoots.

Page 30 How Did They Do It?
This activity could be introduced by playing the adverb game. Pupils could be asked to perform a task, walking across the room, for instance, in the manner of the chosen adverb.

Page 31 Pick and Mix
The words could appear in the poem in any order, but suggest that they appear as close together as possible.

Page 32 Cats and Dogs
Use the same pattern for other groups of weather synonyms, for example, a day gradually becoming hotter.

Page 33 I Mean To Say
The poem can be extended by providing further sub-headings.

Page 34 Opposites
Insist on a reasonably extended conclusion, perhaps by asking for three things that 'I' might do.

Page 35   I Dare You
Recipes and spells are further examples of 'second person' writing.

Pages 36-7   Biker's Brainstorm/Brainstorm Chart
Brainstorming is best introduced with a teacher or special needs assistant acting as scribe. To be successful brainstorming requires prompting by asking questions or filling in categories as in the brainstorm here. The spidergram is one of many possible patterns. Some pupils find a simple series of lists easier to cope with.

Pages 38-9   Drafting Checklist/Drafting in Groups
This sheet can be kept for future reference. For some pupils, producing even one draft is a major achievement and teachers might hesitate to send them away to rewrite. The advantage of poetry is that it is short, which makes the task easier. Pupils should not slavishly work through this checklist, but it is useful to have as a reminder, perhaps reduced to an instruction to stick in an exercise book or enlarged to make a poster.

Page 40   Line Up Again
The poems are cinquains (2-4-6-8-2 syllables per line).

Street Monsters
Lamp posts
Sleep in the streets
Waiting for the evening
To open yellow eyes and come
To life

November Night
Listen ...
With faint dry sound
Like steps of passing ghosts
The leaves, frost-crisped, break from the trees
And fall

Pages 41-2   Talking About Poems/Having Kittens
The first sheet can be kept for future use. The questions offered are not exclusive and are designed merely to initiate discussion. *Having Kittens* may lead to informal storytelling about similar incidents which can lead to writing. (See *Storytelling* on page 27).

Pages 43-5   Performing Poems/ Croc City Rap/ Litter
These poems have been selected for their informality and performance possibilities. Encourage discussion about how they should be performed based on the information in the *Performing Poems* checklist.

Page 46   Poetry Around Us
Pupils should be aware that they listen to and read poetry all the time. Poetry is not just something 'done in school'. Epitaphs, newspaper headlines, playground chants, rhymes in greetings cards, advertising slogans, jokes and tongue twisters, and song lyrics can all be explored. Rhyme, rhythm, repetition, the sound of words and layout can all be explored as writing models.

Page 47   Poetry Presentation.
The four ideas are useful examples of how pupils can make their work more valuable to themselves by taking imaginative pride in its presentation.

Pages 48   Poetry Record Sheet
The best poetry is unexpected, surprising and unpredictable. Because it is intended to affect the reader in some way, poetry is by its nature subjective. Any assessment needs to involve the reader too.

Further reading

The Essential Guide to Poetry by David Orme (Folens, 1 85276191 1) while designed for Primary teachers, will provide much additional guidance for teachers and assistants, particularly if they are not fully confident working with poetry.

Get Into Shape

- Talk about how the shape of each poem looks like the weather it is talking about.

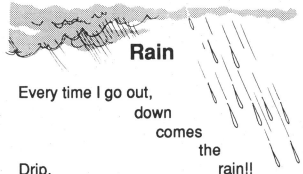

Rain

Every time I go out,
        down
           comes
              the
Drip,   rain!!
   drip,
      drip, down my neck, in my shoes,
cars splash me, my umbrella's got a hole
in it splosh,
      splosh,
        splosh,
          I hate the rain!!!

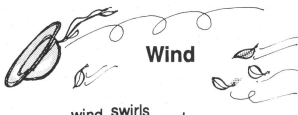

Wind

The wind swirls and twists,

rattling the windows of our houses.

Stealing our hats, delivering leaves to

our front doors like a
              mad
                postman

- Write a poem about your favourite sort of weather.
  Choose a weather shape for your poem.

Today's Weather Forecast _____

Action Shapes

- Work with a partner. Talk about this poem by Ian Blackman.
  Why is the shape of the poem important? How does this poem work?
  What do you think of it?

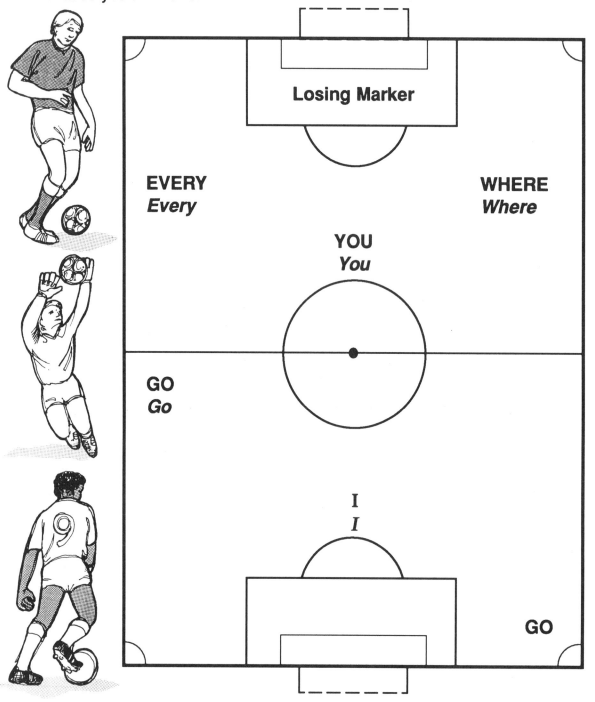

Losing Marker

EVERY
Every

WHERE
Where

YOU
You

GO
Go

I
I

GO

- Here are some ideas for action poems. Turn over and write a poem
  about each of them. Choose a shape for each poem.

  1 Climbing a mountain - and falling off!
  2 Parachuting
  3 Bungee jumping

Noisy Traffic

● Work with a partner. Read the poem carefully.
Underline what you think is special about each line.

Traffic

One   wonky wheelchair wobbling wildly

Two   tatty Toyotas turning

Three   thrilling Thunderbirds throbbing

Four   Ford Fiestas

PURRR

PURRR

● Follow the pattern. Write some more lines to complete the poem.

Five _____

Six _____

Seven _____

Eight _____

Nine _____

Ten _____

NOW   ● Illustrate one of your lines in the box below.

SPECIALS! Poetry

Squelch!

- This poem is written in an alien language.
  The pictures may help you to understand what it is about.

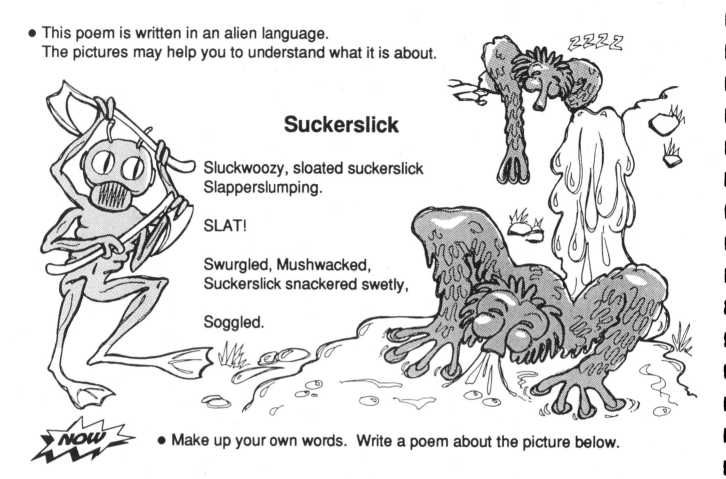

Suckerslick

Sluckwoozy, sloated suckerslick
Slapperslumping.

SLAT!

Swurgled, Mushwacked,
Suckerslick snackered swetly,

Soggled.

- **NOW** ● Make up your own words. Write a poem about the picture below.

_____

_____

_____

_____

_____

_____

_____

_____

_____

Continue over the page ...

SPECIALS! Poetry

Sound Poems

● Read the words. Talk about the kinds of sounds they make and why.

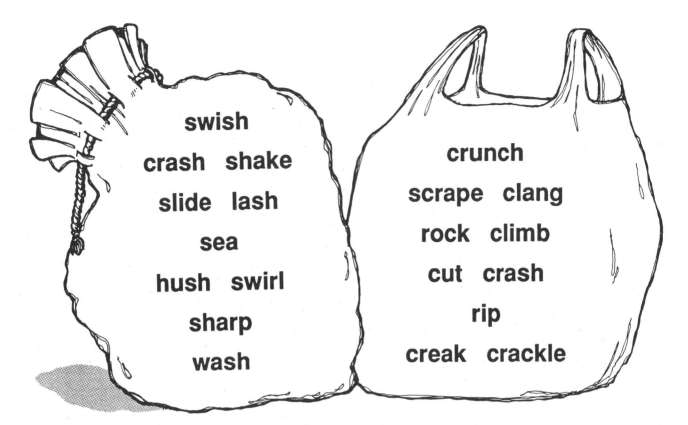

swish

crash shake

slide lash

sea

hush swirl

sharp

wash

crunch

scrape clang

rock climb

cut crash

rip

creak crackle

NOW ● Choose one of these bags of sound words. Write a sound poem using the sound words. You could add some words of your own.

CRACK!BANG!RIP!SWIRL!HUSH!CUT

SHARP!LASH!CLIMB!CRACKLE!CRUNCH!

SPECIALS! Poetry

Liverpool Jam

- Read the poem. Some of the words are missing.
  Talk about words that might fill the gaps.

Liverpool Jam

This is the way to make Liverpool Jam:

One delivery van parked on the hill,

Ten trucks with loads to _____

Twenty tankers delivering fuel,

Thirty wardens enforcing the _____

Forty buses clogging the town,

Fifty policemen slowing them _____

Sixty bicycles crawling along,

Seventy tradesmen with maps all _____

Eighty pedestrians changing the lights,

Ninty tourist seeing the _____

A **Hundred** motorists all saying _____

There's nothing as sticky as Liverpool Jam!

- Choose words that rhyme. Fill in the gaps. Compare your version with
  someone else. Is there only one answer?

- Work with a partner. Talk about ways of performing this poem.

Time For a Rhyme

● Talk about the poem on the gun barrel. Why do you think it has only one word in each line?

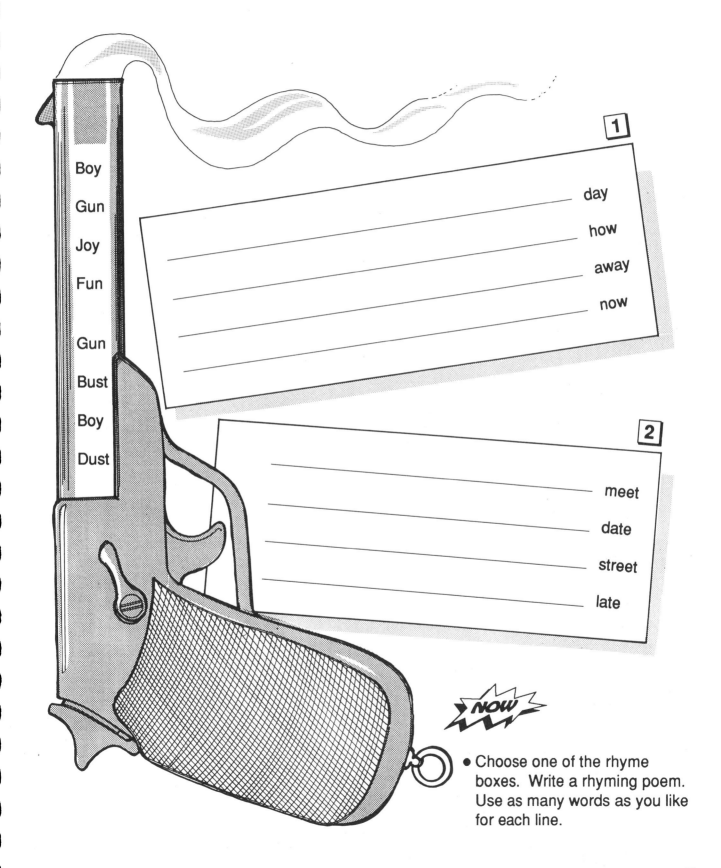

Boy
Gun
Joy
Fun

Gun
Bust
Boy
Dust

1

_____ day
_____ how
_____ away
_____ now

2

_____ meet
_____ date
_____ street
_____ late

NOW

● Choose one of the rhyme boxes. Write a rhyming poem. Use as many words as you like for each line.

Line Up

● Read the poem. Divide it into lines. The rhymes will help.
Write it out correctly on the tombstone.

Fred Smith RIP. He passed the
policeman without any fuss and
he passed the cart of hay,
He tried to pass a swerving bus
and then he passed away.

● Here are two poems without rhymes. Divide them into lines.
Compare your poems with a partner. Is there more than one way to
divide them?

Dust carts revving up; dirty yellow
erasers smudging out rubbish.

Bear-like, the Deputy Head
shambles along the crowded corridor
issuing his orders as sharp cuffs and
growls. Pushing his way towards his
office, he is annoyed by a first year
and growls at it, baring his teeth of
words: 'You boy! Come here!'

SPECIALS! Poetry

Tall Story

● Complete the poem. Choose the best lines from the computer screen.

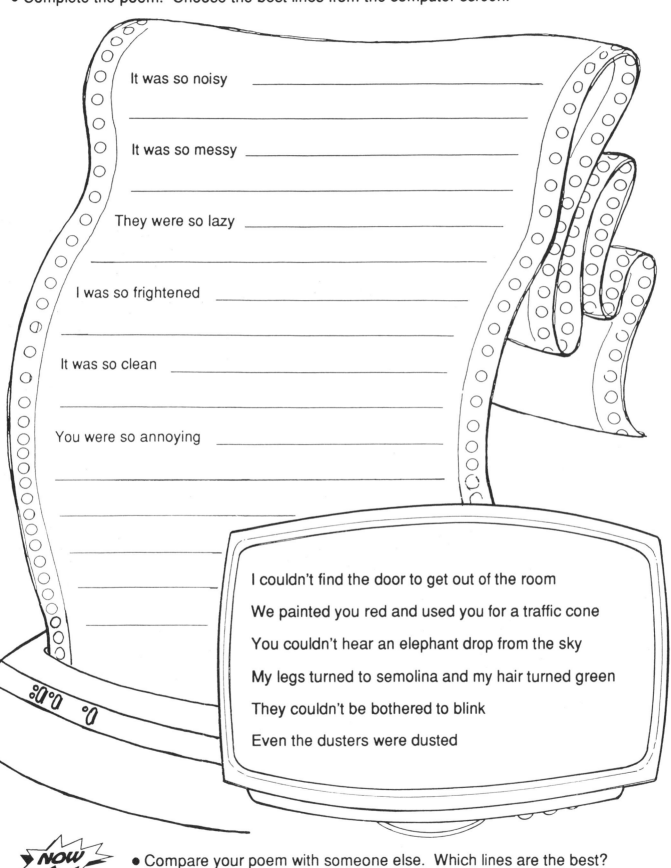

It was so noisy _____

_____

It was so messy _____

_____

They were so lazy _____

_____

I was so frightened _____

_____

It was so clean _____

_____

You were so annoying _____

_____

_____

_____

_____

I couldn't find the door to get out of the room

We painted you red and used you for a traffic cone

You couldn't hear an elephant drop from the sky

My legs turned to semolina and my hair turned green

They couldn't be bothered to blink

Even the dusters were dusted

NOW ● Compare your poem with someone else. Which lines are the best?

I've Got Rhythm

- Read the verses below. They come from a long poem.
  Three men ride to bring the good news to the town of Aix,
  but only one makes it! Roland is the storyteller's horse.

How They Brought the Good News From Ghent To Aix

I sprang to the stirrup, and Joris, and he;

I galloped, Dirk galloped, we galloped all three;

'Good speed!' cried the watch, as the gate-bolts undrew;

'Speed!' echoed the wall to us galloping through;

Behind shut the postern, the lights sank to rest,

And into the midnight we galloped abreast.

Not a word to each other, we kept the great pace

Neck by neck, stride by stride, never changing our place;

I turned in my saddle and made the girths tight,

Then shortened each stirrup, and set the pique right,

Rebuckled the cheek-strap, chained slacker the bit,

Nor galloped less steadily Roland a whit.

by Robert Browning

- Listen carefully to the rhythm of the poem. Why does it fit
  the story?

- Find a way of marking the verses to stress the rhythm.

- What good news do you think the riders were bringing?

- Work with a partner. Talk about ways of performing the poem.

Get Rapping!

● Work with a partner. Read this rap. Talk about ways of performing it.

Everybody Rap

Can you do a rap?
    Can you do a rap?
Can you make a rhyme?
    Can you make a rhyme?
Can you link up words,
    Can you link up words,
To make me blow my mind?
    To help me blow my mind?

Poetry is the thing that we can do
To show that there's no difference
Between me and you.

Black and white are all the same
And those who say different are mad insane.

Do you agree?
    Do you agree?
If you agree,
    Say yowl to me.

by Su Andi

● Write a rap.

| 1 | Choose something to write about. |

| 2 | Write down words that describe your choice. |

| 3 | Find words that sound alike and match them, for example *same* and *insane*. |

| 4 | Add more lines. Remember rhythm is very important. |

● Perform your rap.

Sizzling Syllables

● Listen as you say these words:

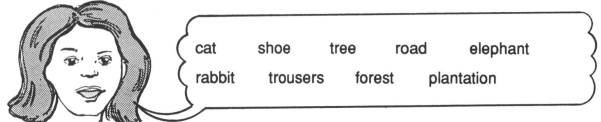

> cat   shoe   tree   road   elephant
>
> rabbit   trousers   forest   plantation

Cat is a one syllable word. **Rab/bit** has two syllables, **El/e/phant** has three.

● How many syllables are there in these words?

Computer	**3**	Horse		Telephone	
Cheese		Tyrannosaurus		Caterpillar	
Bookshelf		Teacher			

● Count the syllables in this poem. Write the numbers in the boxes.
The first two have been done to help you. Find the poem's special pattern.

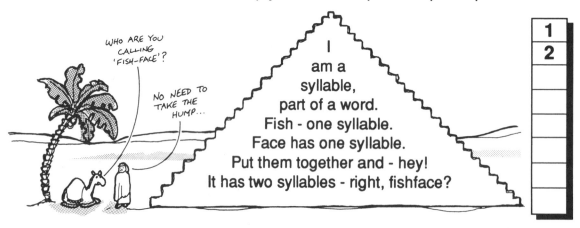

WHO ARE YOU CALLING 'FISH-FACE'?

NO NEED TO TAKE THE HUMP...

> I
> am a
> syllable,
> part of a word.
> Fish - one syllable.
> Face has one syllable.
> Put them together and - hey!
> It has two syllables - right, fishface?

1
2

● Write your own syllable poem. Start like this:

NOW

WHAT RHYMES WITH CAMEL?

> I
> am a

IT DOESN'T NEED TO RHYME...

...FISHFACE

How Haiku Can You Go?

- **Haiku** poems come from Japan. They have a special pattern of syllables.

In the morning air ◄—— 5 syllables

Grass is cold, damp and crunchy. ◄—— 7 syllables

Then out comes the sun. ◄—— 5 syllables

- Count the syllables in these poems. Which poem does not obey the rule?
  Write the numbers in the boxes.

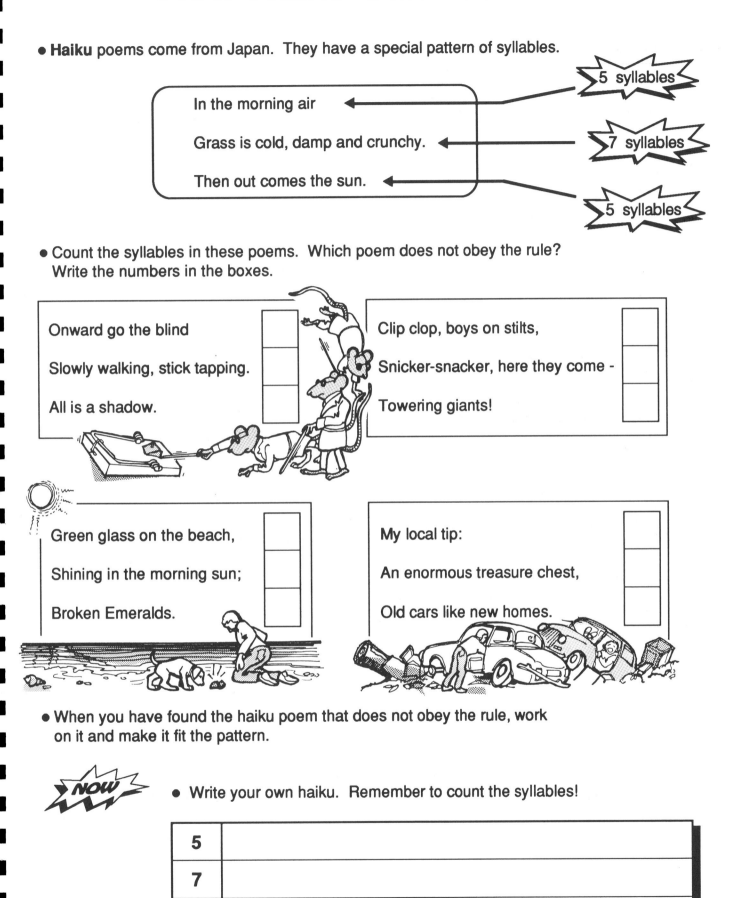

Onward go the blind

Slowly walking, stick tapping.

All is a shadow.

Clip clop, boys on stilts,

Snicker-snacker, here they come –

Towering giants!

Green glass on the beach,

Shining in the morning sun;

Broken Emeralds.

My local tip:

An enormous treasure chest,

Old cars like new homes.

- When you have found the haiku poem that does not obey the rule, work
  on it and make it fit the pattern.

NOW • Write your own haiku. Remember to count the syllables!

5	
7	
5	

SPECIALS! Poetry

Limericks

● Read the limerick below. Work out its pattern.

There was an old person from Crewe
Who found a dead mouse in his stew.
Said the waiter, 'Don't shout
And wave it about,
Or the rest will be wanting one too!'

1 **Length.**

● How many lines does it have? Write the number in the box.

2 **Rhyme pattern.**

● Which words rhyme with Crewe? _____

● Which word rhymes with shout? _____

3 **Rhythm.**

● Tap out the rhythm of a limerick.

OOF!

Our teacher's as blind as a bat

● Write some limericks of your own. The first lines are given to help you.

It happened one day at [_____] school

_____

_____

_____

_____

There was a young [_____] from Bengal

_____

_____

_____

SPECIALS! Poetry

Match Them Up

● These limericks have the last line missing.
  Choose a last line for each one. Use the suggestions below.

There was an old man from Peru
Who complained he had nothing to do,
So to remain entertained
He regularly trained

A surly young fellow from Hyde
In a funeral procession was spied,
When asked, 'Who is dead?'
He giggled and said

There was a fat lady of Ryde,
Whose shoelaces once came untied.
She feared that to bend
Would display her rear end

A humorous man-eating shark
Lived just off the island of Sark.
He told awful jokes
To nautical blokes

✂ - - - - - - - - - - -

But his bite was worse than his bark.	I don't know, I just came for the ride.
So she cried and she cried and she cried.	By boiling his head in a stew.
And finished by having a chew.	But it only came out after dark.
And there's some things it's better to hide.	By beating his kids with a shoe.
Which was monstrous and thirty feet wide.	She blew bubbles and danced in a bin.
Then exploded because of a spark.	So she sat on the cooker and fried.
By fighting the beasts in the zoo.	Then bit off their feet for a lark.
Her dentures got stuck in the tin.	He never could eat them - he'd tried.

● Compare your answers with someone else. Which are the best lines? Why?

Poems Alive!

● In poems, ordinary things can come to life. Talk about these descriptions.

The old tree stretched out its branches like a witch scratching a victim with her fingernails.

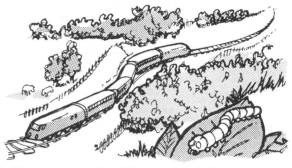

The train looked like a brightly coloured caterpillar.

The snow lay piled up like a sleepy polar bear.

The wind howled with rage and spitefully tore down chimneys.

NOW ● Write four poetry descriptions in the boxes.

The chainsaw ——————	The motor-bike ——————
The submarine ——————	The fog ——————

Riddles

- Work with a partner. Talk about these riddles. What do they mean?
  Write the answers in the boxes.

What am I?

I am a serpent.
On hot days, I lie
in lazy coils
In the sunshine:
My body is long and long.
I am greedy for water,
And when I drink
I hiss my pleasure.

_____

You won't catch me,
For I'm an underwater
knight
In silver armour.

_____

I have no gun, but I'll still take your money.
If you hit me, my silver teeth come rolling out;
Then I get angry and take them all back.
I have one arm, and glowing eyes that roll round and round.
I have the biggest pocket you ever saw!

_____

- Talk about how riddles work.

- Write your own riddles. Test them out on a friend.

A clock

I am a three
handed teacher...

_____

_____

_____

A television

Look me straight in the eye...

_____

_____

_____

_____

_____

Dirty Dustbins

● Work in a small group. Talk about the poem. Here are some ideas:

1 If you met the poet, what questions would you like to ask him?

2 Do you think a dustbin is a good subject for a poem? If not, why not?

3 The flies seem almost human in this poem. How has the poet managed this?

4 Which parts of the poem did you especially like?
Are there any parts you did not like? Why?

5 Three phrases have been <u>underlined</u>. Talk about what they mean.

Hi Mr Fly

This is our city.
On hot days,
When rope smells shake the air
Like factory hooters,
We are open for business.
Inside our black plastic walls,
We recycle your leavings
Into pure white maggots,
Then relax over a drink
In your squashed cola can.
Those old bones
Are **fast food joints** for us.
How we love to dribble
On those chewy bits of fat
You left at the side of your plate,
Crush it to juice with our feet,
Syphon it into our mouth
Like strawberry milkshake.
Please!
Don't bang down that lid,
We get a **real buzz**
Out of your rubbish

NOW ● Imagine you are an animal or insect. Write a poem of your own.
Tell your story.

First Lines

● Work in groups. Choose one of these first lines to start a poem. The next person must continue after three lines.

 The leaves were a pile of lost treasure...

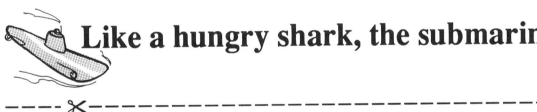 *The sea is a hungry polar bear...*

 The old tree bent in the wind like...

 Like a hungry shark, the submarine ...

The moon is a ghostly galleon...

Humming like a top...

● Write out your group poems.

● Compare your poem with another group's. How did the poem develop?

● Draw the pictures that the lines suggest.

Storytelling

Here is a true story told by Nicola:

> When I got home the other day I found I had forgotten my key! I was desperate to go to the loo! I tried all the windows but they were locked. The upstairs bathroom window was open, so I got the ladder from the shed and put it up. The end of the ladder broke the window! Then my Dad rushed out. He had come home early and was in the house all the time. He was furious with me. 'Why didn't you just ring the bell?!'

● Nicola used the story in a poem. Talk about how she used her story.

OH NO!
I've forgotten my key,
and I'm
DESPERATE
For the loo!
Try the windows.
Locked.
Locked.
Locked.
Locked.
OPEN! but it's upstairs!
I'M STILL DESPERATE!
Get the ladder,
Careful...

SMASH!!!

ON NO!
Why didn't I just ring the bell?
Dad was home all the time!

● Work with a partner. Tell the story of something funny that has happened to you. Ask your partner to write it down. Make a poem of your funny story.

Comic Strip Poem

● Look at the comic strip poem called *Dirty Dog* by Peter Dixon.

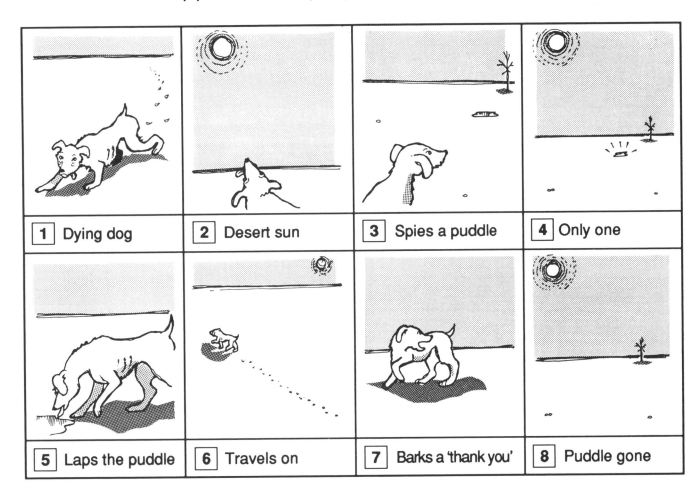

| 1 Dying dog | 2 Desert sun | 3 Spies a puddle | 4 Only one |
| 5 Laps the puddle | 6 Travels on | 7 Barks a 'thank you' | 8 Puddle gone |

● Draw pictures for this comic strip poem.

| 1 We're going to score! | 2 Want to bet? | 3 Where's the ball? | 4 In the net. |

● Write and draw your own comic strip poem.

Telling a Story

- Work in a small group. Read the verses.
  Cut out and assemble the poem correctly.

Edward

'Why does your brand so drop with blood, Edward, Edward? Why does your brand so drop with blood, And why so sad gang ye, O?'	'A what penance will you do for that, Edward, Edward. What penance will you do for that? My dear son, now tell me, O.'
'O I have killed my hawk so good, Mother, mother. O I have killed my hawk so good, And I have no more but he, O.'	'I'll set my feet on yonder boat, Mother, mother. I'll set my feet on yonder boat, And I'll fare over the sea, O.'
'Your hawk's blood was never so red, Edward, Edward. Your hawk's blood was never so red, My dear so, I tell thee, O.'	'What will you leave to your bairns and wife, Edward, Edward? What will you leave to your bairns and wife, When you go over the sea, O?'
'O I have killed my red-roan horse, Mother, mother. O I have killed my red-roan horse, That was so far and free, O.'	'The world's room. Let them beg through life, Mother, mother. The world's room. Let them beg through life, For them no more I'll see, O.'
Your horse was old, and you have got more, Edward, Edward. Your horse was old, and you have got more, Some other deed you did, O.'	'And what will you leave to your own mother dear, Edward, Edward? And what will you leave to your own mother dear, My dear so, now tell me, O.'
O I have killed my father dear, Mother, mother. O I have killed my father dear, Alas and woe is me, O.'	'The curse of Hell from me you shall bear, Mother, mother. The curse of Hell from me you shall bear, Such counsel you gave me, O!'

- How do you know your version is correct?

- Underline any words you do not understand. Look them up in a dictionary.

- Why does the poem sound so strange?

- When you think you understand the story, talk about why Edward might have murdered his father. You could write a poem about it.

SPECIALS! Poetry   © Folens

Time For a Verb

Verbs are **action** words, They are good for **action** poems.

- Choose a subject for an action poem from the pictures.
  Add more verbs to the list before you start your action poem.

swerved	flashed	shot
accelerated	deafened	bounced

 • Write an action poem. You do not have to use all the verbs in your poem.

SPECIALS! Poetry

How Did They Do It?

Adverbs are words that describe verbs, for example 'the girl walked *quickly*'.

- Work with a partner. Look at the picture and the adverbs.
  Talk about which of the adverbs you could use in a poem about the picture.
  Put a tick (✓) or a cross (✗) beside them.

angrily ☐	lazily ☐	loudly ☐	nervously ☐
roughly ☐	fast ☐	fearfully ☐	gently ☐
willingly ☐	unwillingly ☐	fiercely ☐	honestly ☐

- Write a poem about the picture. Use the adverbs from the list.

SPECIALS! Poetry

Pick and Mix

● Throw some dice to find one **naming** word (a noun), one **action** word (a verb) and one **describing** word (an adjective or adverb). Do this several times.

Naming word (Noun)		Action word (Verb)		Describing word (Adjective/Adverb)	
wind	⚀	to dream	⚀	brightly	⚀
stone	⚁	to struggle	⚁	whispering	⚁
eye	⚂	to shake	⚂	ghostly	⚂
star	⚃	to crumble	⚃	deeply	⚃
ruin	⚄	to bend	⚄	wicked	⚄
flame	⚅	to roar	⚅	grey	⚅

NOW ● Write a short poem using the three kinds of word in each line.

Cats and Dogs

• Put these **rain words** in order. Write them in the boxes.
  Finish the poem by saying what you are doing or what is happening when it rains.

drizzling

coming down in buckets

spitting

showering

dripping

spotting

pouring

It's   *spitting*

The people in the street start to put up

their umbrellas.

It's _____

I _____

_____

It's _____

The _____

_____

It's _____

I _____

_____

It's _____

The _____

_____

It's _____

I _____

_____

It's _____

The _____

_____

SPECIALS! Poetry

I Mean To Say

- You use 'I' in writing when:
  - you write about yourself
  - you write about what you did, perhaps in a story.

- Write a passport poem about yourself.

Me

PASSPORT

I hate _____

_____

But I really like _____

_____

I wish _____

_____

But I'm really worried that _____

_____

One day I'll _____

_____

Just so long as I don't _____

_____

NOW • Compare your passport poem with someone else. How are you different?

Opposites

You can use 'I' to pretend to be someone else, for example an animal.

● Read this poem. Talk about how it works and write a line to finish it.

I am a cobra.
With my hypnotising eyes,
And poison fangs,
I _____

_____

NOW ● Write two 'I' poems. Make them show opposite characters, for example good and bad, girl and boy, young and old. Use the word patterns below to help.

I am a _____

With my _____

And _____

I _____

I am a _____

With my _____

And _____

I _____

I Dare You

We use 'you' when we speak to someone directly, for example 'I hate **you**!'

We can use 'you' when we give instructions, for example '**You** turn into Station Road.'

● Read the *double-dare* poem. Add some more ideas.

Why don't you...
Climb up the outside of the Empire State building?
You're a chicken if you don't!

Why don't you...
Pretend you're superman and run head first into a brick wall?
You're a chicken if you don't!

Why don't you...
_____
_____

Why don't you...
_____
_____

Why don't you...
_____
_____

Why don't you...
_____
_____

NOW ● Turn over. Continue your poem for two more verses. Compare your poem with someone else. Which was the best? Why?

Biker's Brainstorm

Before we write a poem, we need to collect together words and ideas on the subject. This is called **brainstorming**.

● Here is the start of a brainstorm about a motorbike journey. Think of some more ideas to add. Write them on the brainstorm.

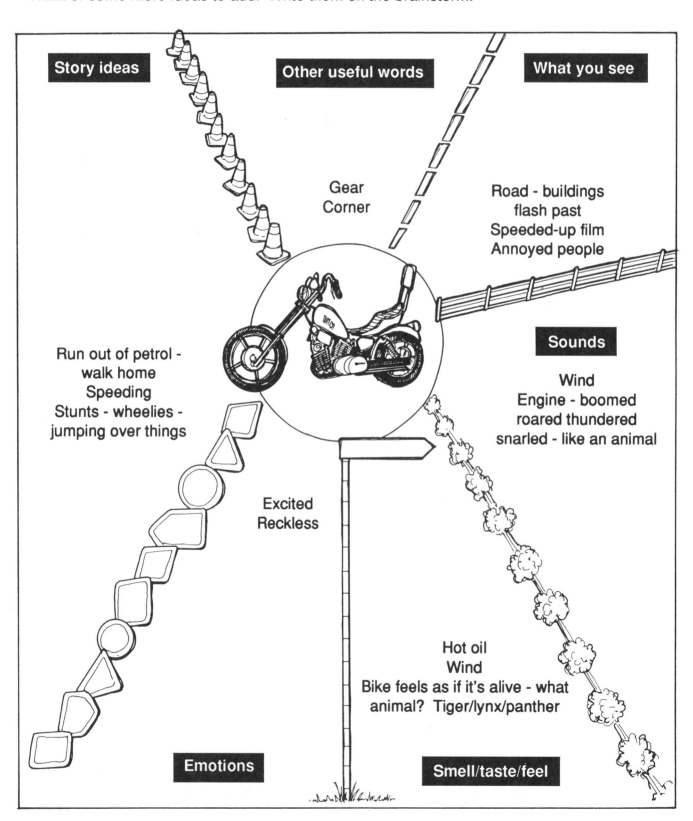

Story ideas

Other useful words

Gear
Corner

What you see

Road - buildings
flash past
Speeded-up film
Annoyed people

Run out of petrol -
walk home
Speeding
Stunts - wheelies -
jumping over things

Sounds

Wind
Engine - boomed
roared thundered
snarled - like an animal

Excited
Reckless

Hot oil
Wind
Bike feels as if it's alive - what
animal? Tiger/lynx/panther

Emotions

Smell/taste/feel

Brainstorm Chart

- Choose a subject for a poem. Think of as many ideas and words as you can on the subject. Write them in the brainstorming box. The headings will help you.

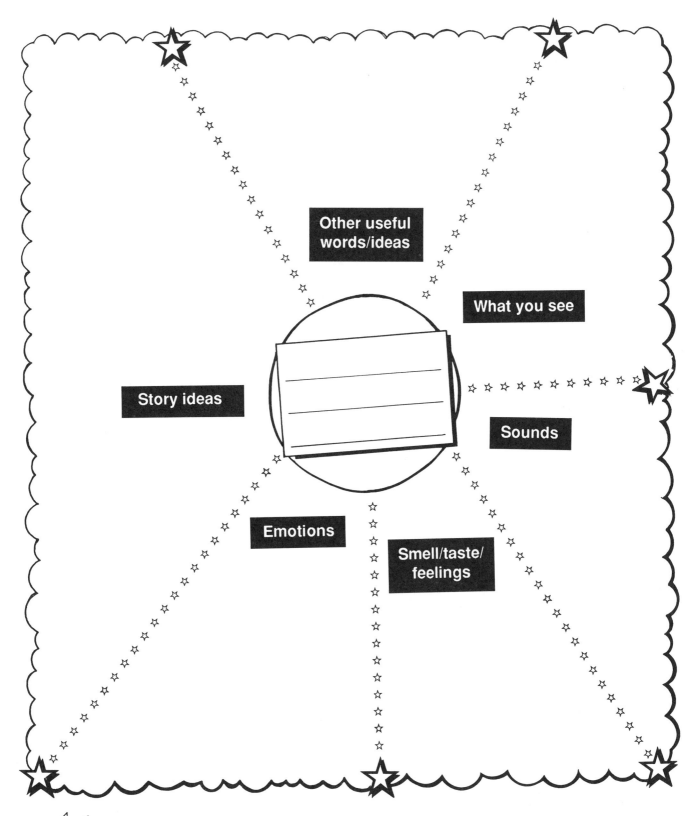

Other useful words/ideas

What you see

Story ideas

Sounds

Emotions

Smell/taste/ feelings

NOW ● Write your poem. Use the words and ideas from your brainstorm.

Drafting Checklist

Name: _____

1

Read your poem through.
Ask yourself:

What did you want to say?
Do you think you have said it?

2

Are there any words you are not happy with? Underline them.
Do you need all of the words?
Can you miss out any?

4

If you have used rhyme, do all the rhymes make sense?
Do rhymes make the poem better?

3

Are there any interesting comparisons and unusual word pictures in the poem?

5

Have you used a special pattern?
Have you got it right?

6

Have you thought about where your lines end?

8

Does your poem have a good ending or does it fizzle out?

7

Have you used punctuation?
Are your choices the right ones?

9

Does your poem sound right when you read it aloud? Underline any parts you are not happy with.

10

Have you checked your poem for spelling and accuracy?

NOW • Ask for help before you make a neat copy.

Drafting in Groups

● Work in small groups. Talk about this first draft of a motorbike ride poem.
Look at your **Drafting Checklist**. Talk about how you would improve the poem.

 ● Write your improved version of the poem in the space.

Motorbike ride

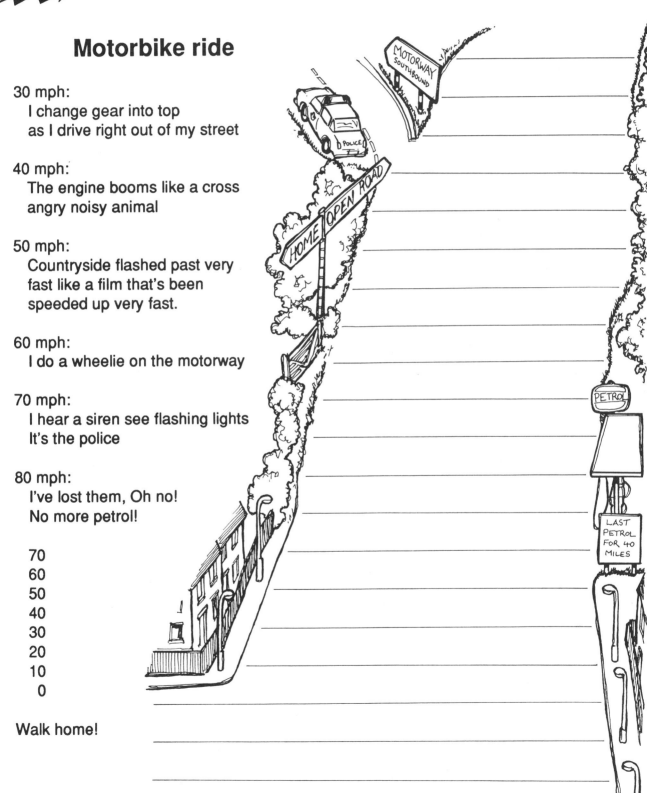

30 mph:
   I change gear into top
   as I drive right out of my street

40 mph:
   The engine booms like a cross
   angry noisy animal

50 mph:
   Countryside flashed past very
   fast like a film that's been
   speeded up very fast.

60 mph:
   I do a wheelie on the motorway

70 mph:
   I hear a siren see flashing lights
   It's the police

80 mph:
   I've lost them, Oh no!
   No more petrol!

   70
   60
   50
   40
   30
   20
   10
    0

Walk home!

Line Up Again

- Read the poems. The lines are in the wrong order. Write them out correctly

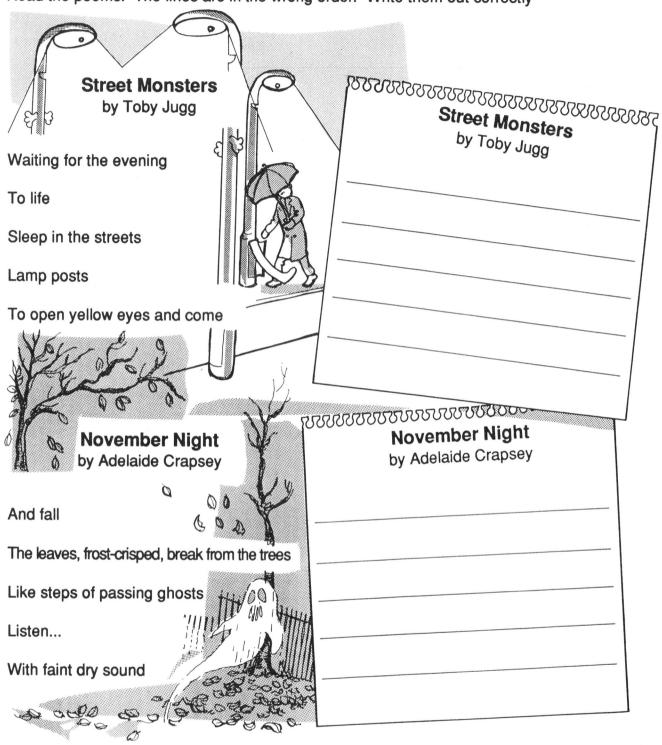

Street Monsters
by Toby Jugg

Waiting for the evening

To life

Sleep in the streets

Lamp posts

To open yellow eyes and come

Street Monsters
by Toby Jugg

November Night
by Adelaide Crapsey

And fall

The leaves, frost-crisped, break from the trees

Like steps of passing ghosts

Listen...

With faint dry sound

November Night
by Adelaide Crapsey

- Both poems should have the same pattern. When you have worked out
  what the pattern is, ask your teacher what this kind of poem is called.

NOW

- Write a poem using the pattern.

SPECIALS! Poetry

Talking About Poems

Name: _____

- Poems sometimes seem difficult at first. The best thing is to talk about them in groups. Read the rules for talking in groups.

Rules for talking in groups

1	Take it in turns to speak.
2	If you disagree, say so but not in a rude way!
3	Ask questions if you do not understand.
4	Listen as well as speaking.
5	Do not try to take over!
6	Think before you speak!

- Here are some questions you could ask about any poem.

1 Does the poem have difficult words? Write them down and find out what they mean.
2 Does the poem have a special pattern? What is it?
3 Does the poem have a story? What is it?
4 Are any of these words helpful in describing the poem?

funny	sad	old-fashioned
serious	angry	simple
descriptive	realistic	difficult

5 What feelings do you think the poet had when writing the poem? Here are some possible feelings:

| sad | amused | nostalgic (thinking about the 'good old days') |
| angry | happy | |

- Here are some questions to ask yourself about the poem.

1 If you met the poet, what would you ask about the poem?
2 Does the poem remind you of anything that has happened to you?

Having Kittens

- Work in a small group. Talk about this poem. Use the **Talking About Poems** sheet.

Having Kittens

When our cat had kittens my
father said we couldn't keep them.

So after we had gone to bed he put
them in a sack and drowned them in

The water butt. Next day I hear
Them mewing in the garden, over and

over, crying for help. I went and
told him. 'Impossible,' he said.

'I've given them away.' I went back
down the garden, hearing them crying pitifully.

I fetched the garden spade and
started digging, digging everywhere.

I couldn't find them. Out he came, all
angry: 'What d'you think you're doing?'

Then he heard them. Started digging
like a navvy. Up it came, the dripping

sack, the kittens crying. He plunged
them in the water butt for several

minutes; long enough to drown a tiger,
let alone a little kitten. 'There,' he

said, 'That's done the trick. Now you
can bury them.' I did. Stuck up a cross:

'Four kittens murdered here,
Sunday the 4th of August, 1953.'

by Phil Powley

- Use what you have learned to write your own poem about something personal that happened to you.

SPECIALS! Poetry

© Folens

Performing Poems

Name: _____

1
Learn as much of the poem as you can! You might not be able to learn it by heart, but you will perform much better if you know it well.

2
Do not hide your head in the copy of the poem! Look at the audience!

4
Think about using your **hands** and **body**.

3
Do not read too quickly.

5 If the poem has a special rhythm, practise until you get it right.

6
Could you use percussion instruments - drums, tambourines - to improve the performance?

8
Perform to a small group first, and listen to what they say.

7
Try and get the right **feeling** in your voice. Do not read a sad poem in a funny voice!

9
If you work with a group, decide:
- How are you going to divide up the poem?
- Are some parts suitable for reading by more than one person?

10
Perform it in different ways until you find the way you are happy with.

NOW
• Enjoy your performance!

Croc City Rap

- Work in a small group. Talk about ways of performing this poem.
  Use your **Performing Poems** checklist to help.

Croc City Rap

Beneath the streets of New York
   there are sewers that stretch for miles,
they say that the sewers of New York
   are filled with crocodiles
and alligators that frightened folk
   have just flushed down the pan,
when the creatures stopped being babies
   and started snapping at their hands.

Chorus:

Croc City,
down below when the city sleeps,
croc city,
snapping away to a hip hop beat
croc city.

Pity the poor sewer walker
   taking his nightly stroll,
thinking about hot coffee
   at the end of his dark patrol.
Then out of the slime, a snapper
   raises its ugly head,
how fast can you sprint down a sewer pipe
   when a crocodile wants you dead...

Croc city,
down below when the city sleeps,
croc city,
snapping away to a hip hop beat
croc city.

The State department issues advice
   to those who find a croc,
whatever you do don't go after it,
   don't chase it with a rock.
Don't start thinking you're Dundee
   out to catch a snapper.
If he opens his mouth, then you can be
   sure this croc, he ain't no rapper!

Croc city,
down below when the city sleeps,
croc city,
snapping away to a hip hop beat,
croc city.

Croc city,
down below when the city sleeps,
croc city,
snapping away to a hip hop beat,
croc city.

Croc city, croc city, croc city,
croc city, croc city,
CROCK CITY...YEAH!

by Brian Moses

NOW • Perform *Croc City Rap*.

Litter

- Work in a small group on a performance of this poem by Levi Tafari.
  Use your **Performing Poems** checklist to help.

Litter

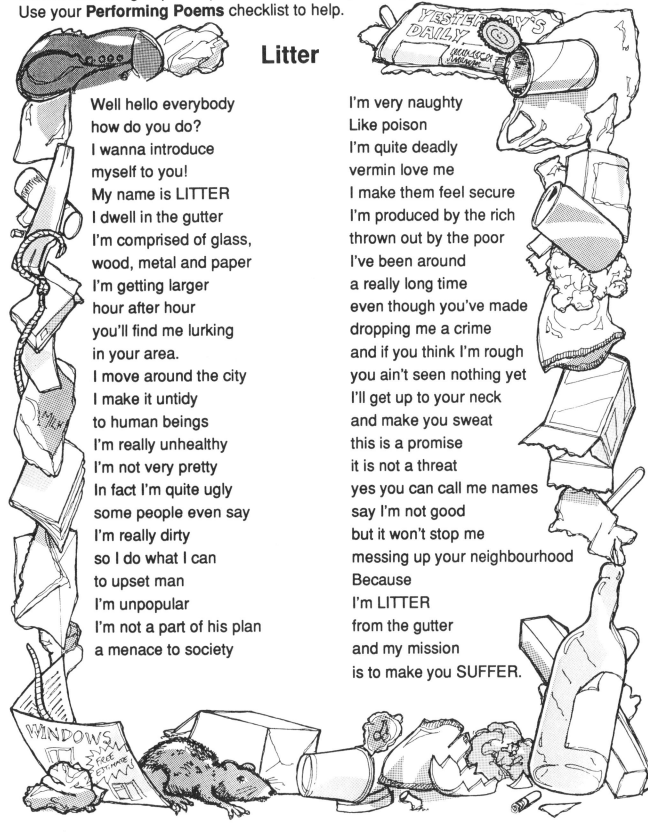

Well hello everybody
how do you do?
I wanna introduce
myself to you!
My name is LITTER
I dwell in the gutter
I'm comprised of glass,
wood, metal and paper
I'm getting larger
hour after hour
you'll find me lurking
in your area.
I move around the city
I make it untidy
to human beings
I'm really unhealthy
I'm not very pretty
In fact I'm quite ugly
some people even say
I'm really dirty
so I do what I can
to upset man
I'm unpopular
I'm not a part of his plan
a menace to society

I'm very naughty
Like poison
I'm quite deadly
vermin love me
I make them feel secure
I'm produced by the rich
thrown out by the poor
I've been around
a really long time
even though you've made
dropping me a crime
and if you think I'm rough
you ain't seen nothing yet
I'll get up to your neck
and make you sweat
this is a promise
it is not a threat
yes you can call me names
say I'm not good
but it won't stop me
messing up your neighbourhood
Because
I'm LITTER
from the gutter
and my mission
is to make you SUFFER.

- Discuss what you think made this
  performance a success or not.

Poetry Around Us

- Poetry is all around us. Work in pairs. Read these poems.
  Talk about where you would find them. Do you think of them as poems? Why?

Dear Passerby,
I beg you please,
Do not hang around.
I did one night,
Caught a cold,
And now I'm underground

ONE POTATO, TWO POTATO,
THREE POTATO, FOUR....

Humpty Dumpty sits on his rug,
Humpty Dumpty's as snug as a bug,
Even on cold days, he's warmed by the sun,
Glazing with Ray is the best thing he's done.

Andi n' Heather
♥ true luv
4ever

- Carry out a survey of poetry in your environment.
  Compare your findings with other people.

What I found

It said ...

Why it is poetry or not

SPECIALS! Poetry

© Folens

Presenting Poetry

● Here are some ways to make your poems look interesting.

Poetry on shapes

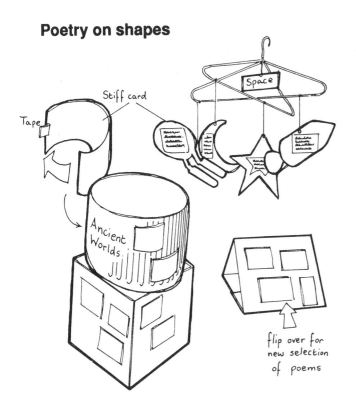

Tape

Stiff card

Space

Ancient Worlds.

flip over for new selection of poems

Silhouette books

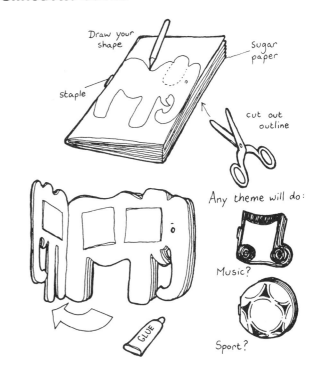

Draw your shape

staple

Sugar paper

cut out outline

Any theme will do:

Music?

Sport?

GLUE

A poetry wheel

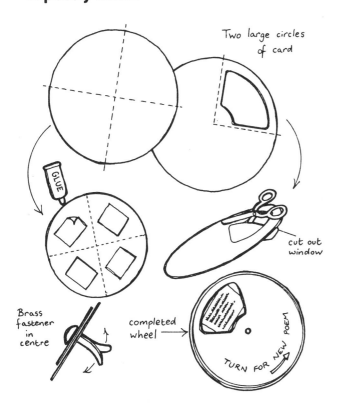

Two large circles of card

GLUE

cut out window

Brass fastener in centre

completed wheel

TURN FOR NEW POEM

A surprise poem

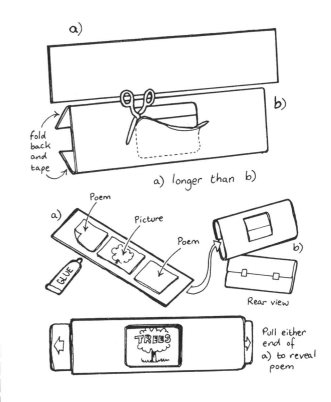

a)

b)

fold back and tape

a) longer than b)

Poem

Picture

Poem

GLUE

Rear view

b)

TREES

Pull either end of a) to reveal poem

Poetry Record Sheet

Title of poem _____

Name of poet _____

- Was the poem easy to read and understand? ☐ Yes ☐ No

- Was the poem suitable for your age.

  Or was it too simple? ☐ Suitable ☐ Too Simple

- What did you do to help you understand the poem?

  Look up difficult words? ☐

  Talk about the poem in groups or class? ☐

  Other: _____

  _____

- Think of one word to describe the feeling in the poem. [   ]

- What did you particularly like about the poem? _____

  _____

- What did you not like about it? _____

  _____

- Did any one you worked with think differently? Ask them what they thought and write down what they say.

  Name _____

  What they thought _____

  _____

- Anything else you would like to say about the poem. _____

  _____